To Olivia
Sandra Hall

S0-BZD-129

THIS BOOK
BELONGS
IN THE NEST OF
OLIVIA

For Nathan, Rachel and Christian

May you always find your way home

Written and illustrated by Sandra Hall

It's always good to go home. The swallows flew excitedly, swooping and chatting, looking forward to arriving at the place where they were born. The big, old carriage house near the harbor offered shelter from the wind and rain and predators. Once safely inside, they could build their nests high up in the ceiling beams.

Almost home! As they flew over the harbor, there stood the carriage house with the doors tightly closed. They flew frantically around the building tapping on the windows with their beaks. Exhausted from a long migration, they perched on the window sill to look inside. The carriage house was empty, all swept clean and last year's nests removed from the ceiling beams. During the winter months, while the swallows were gone, the house and carriage house had been sold. The new family cleaned out the old barn-swallow nests and closed the doors so they could not fly in.

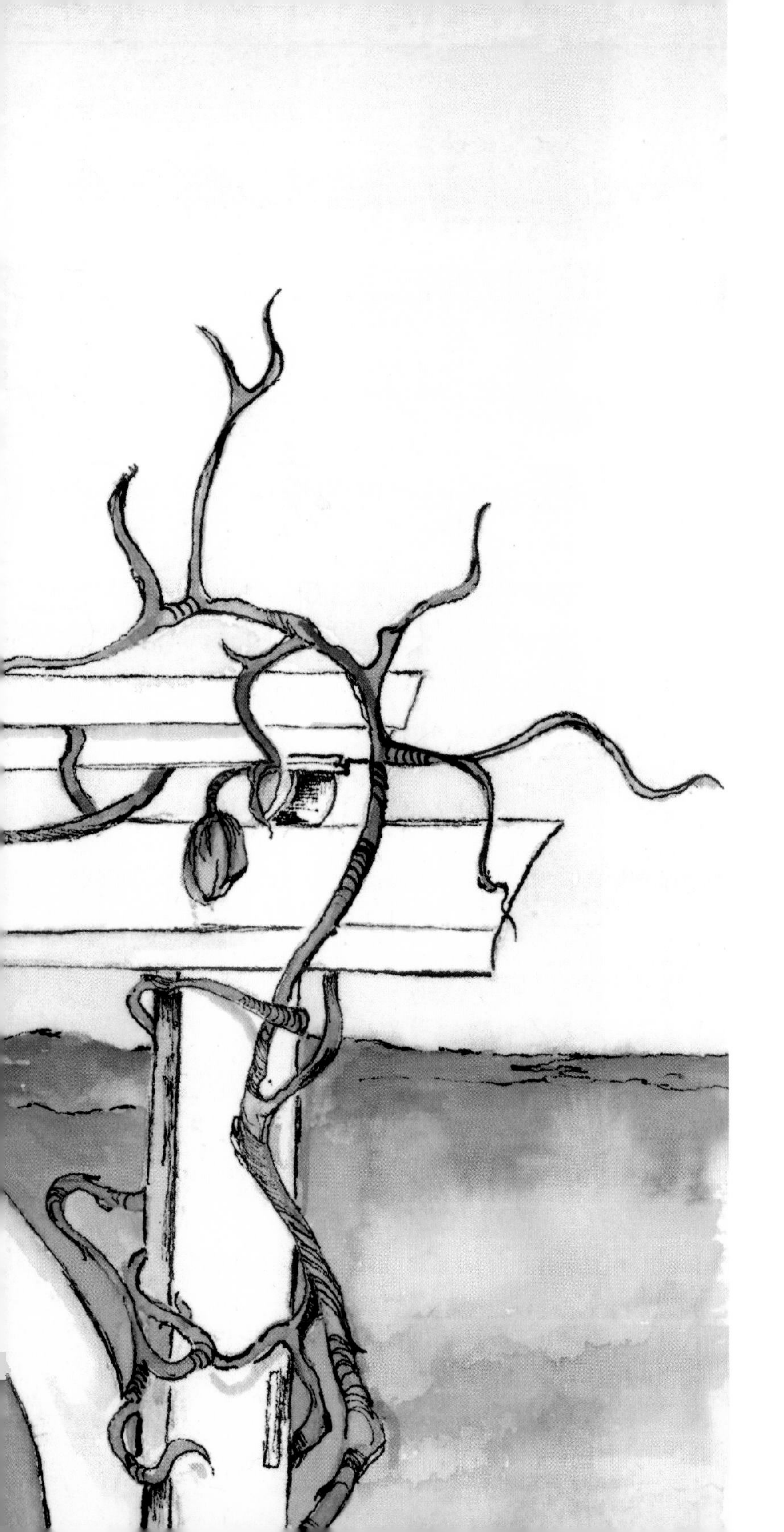

Discouraged, they flew around the house to the garden, where they sat on the gate, clicking and chirping, trying to decide what to do. Something caught the eye of one of the swallows, and he called out to warn the other birds.

As if things weren't bad enough, the new family had a cat! If the swallows could not build their nests high up in the carriage house, this was going to be a challenge. They sat on the garden gate for a long time, chatting among themselves and watching the cat from a high place. The big tiger cat paid no attention to them.

The barn swallows noticed that the cat was very busy gathering leaves and bits of grass. He carried them close to the house and piled them up neatly to make a cozy… nest! A leaf nest! How bad could things be if the cat knows how to build a leaf nest for himself? Maybe the swallows would be welcome here after all.

Instinct is a strong and wonderful thing. The swallows flew around the house one more time and decided, just for one night, to claim the side porch for shelter. Things would be better in the morning, and so they tucked their heads under their wings and went to sleep—dreaming of nests. By morning the barn swallows decided to stay.

THE RECIPIE TO Build A Good NEST
1. Pick A high place under the EAVES OR IN A BARN.
2 MAKE SURE YOU HAVE A Pond nearby AND GRASSES And Twigs to build with.
3. Pack your mud tightly to MAKE A strong NEST.
4. Look for feathers dropped by LARGER birds to MAKE A soft Lining.
5. Get IN AND MAKE SURE you fit.

The day began early and the work went on until dark. The swallows were busy collecting straw and building a mud nest by making many flights to a small pond nearby. They used their beaks to scoop up water and make the mud that holds their home together. The side porch they had chosen offered good, high shelter, and the swallow family started a new life together.

The days passed quickly and the nest building went on at a fast pace. The little swallows spent their days swooping and turning in and out of the porch. The people watched them and the cat continued to build his own leaf nest. Life went on very nicely for everyone. After all, swallows traditionally bring good luck to any house!

Then one day things became quieter on the swallows' porch. A quick look while the swallows were out hunting showed the people that there were eggs in the mud nest! That's when the sign went up: "Please use the front door, nesting in progress. Thanks." A ribbon was tied across the porch steps, and the swallows knew they were safe and welcome!

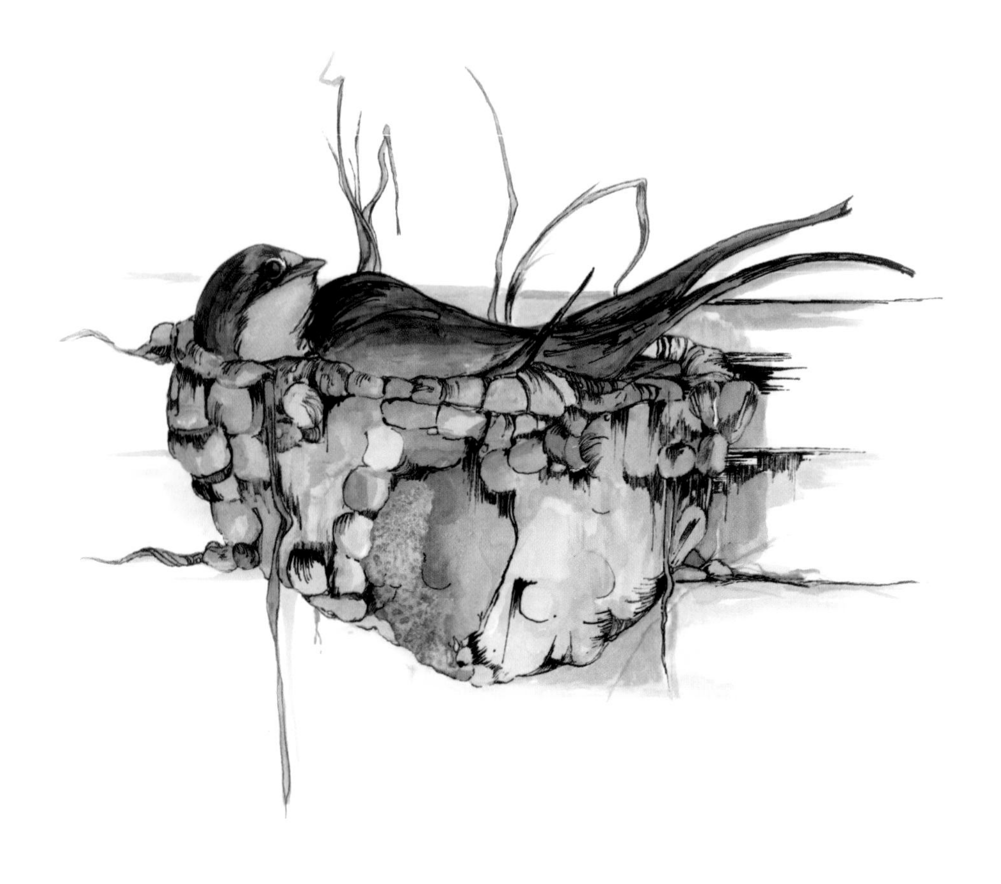

Each day came with the anticipation of baby swallows. The people in the house wondered how many there would be and when they would arrive. Mother swallow began to spend more and more time on the nest. Suddenly tiny chirping voices could be heard! Five to be exact!

The days became a shared routine. Barn swallows are very attentive parents and took turns hunting and feeding the five babies. Before long the good care started to show with bright eyes and feathers appearing. The proud parents would fly and whirl and call out with loud chirping!

Baby barn swallows grow quickly and become hungrier everyday. Little spurts of feathers grew sleek and shiny. Wings became stronger.

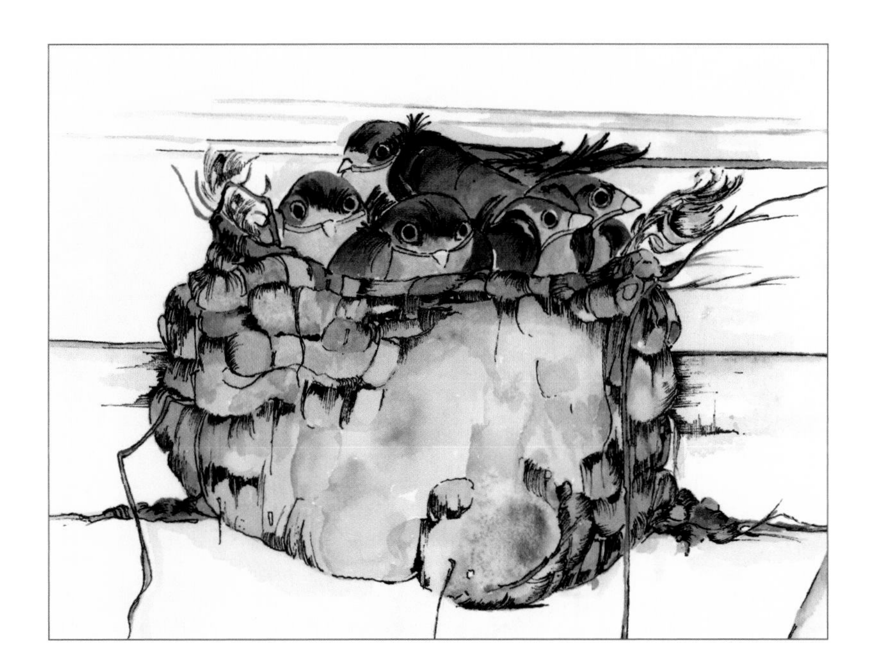

It was fun to watch them inside the cozy nest. As the babies grew bigger, the nest seemed to grow smaller. Soon it would be time to fly. Once again the parents began to plan for that big day.

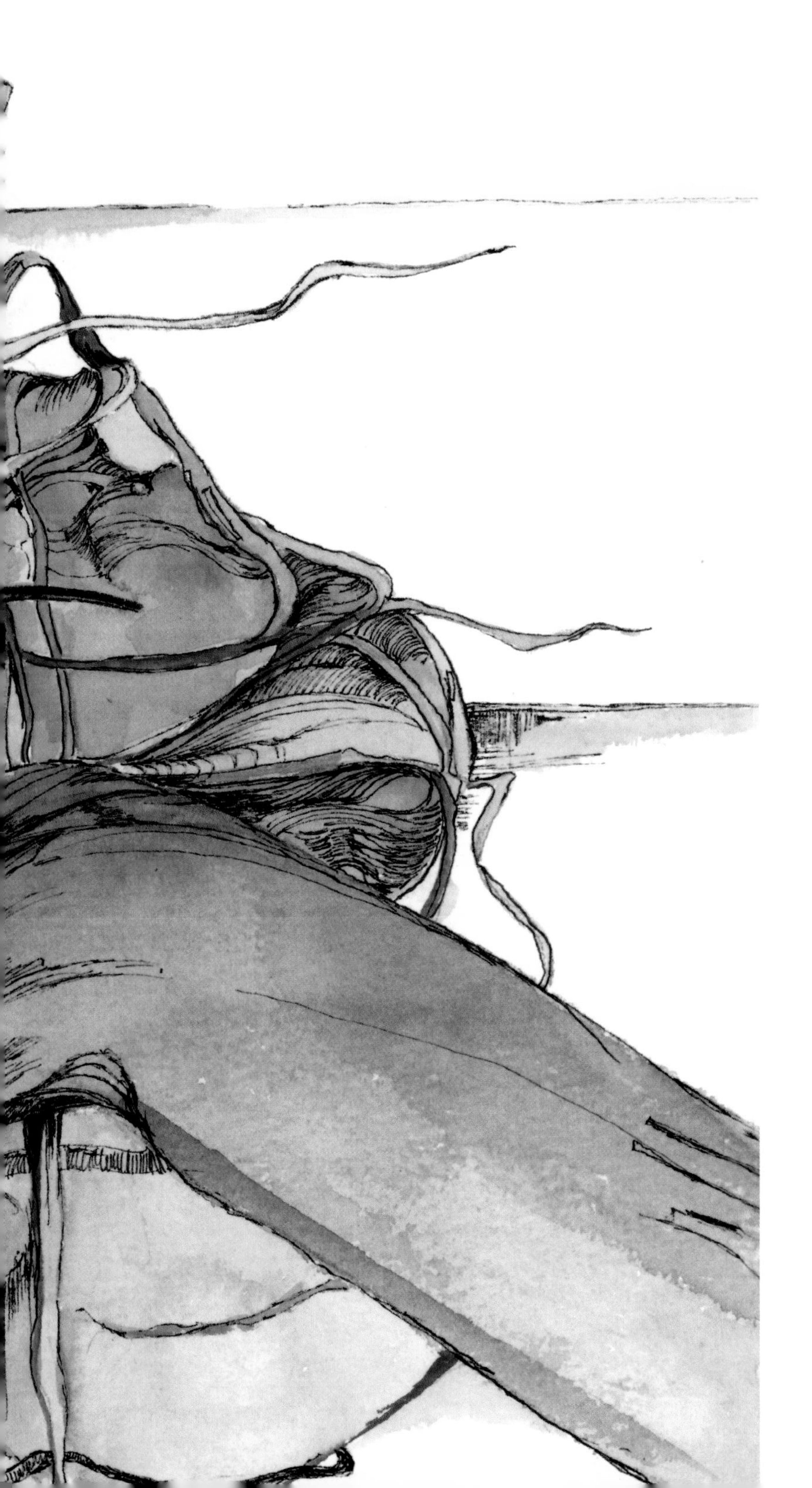

When the day to fly arrived, the entire swallow family was excited! The swallow parents flew and coached each little bird out of the nest. Some made a leap and flew a short distance. Some were not too sure and stood on the side of the nest flapping their little wings. By the end of the morning, though, the nest was empty and all the baby swallows were flying!

The people in the house watched and worried. What if something happens to them? What if a baby swallow falls to the ground or gets lost? All through the day the people would check the nest, missing the little birds.

The day wore on to twilight when all of a sudden cries of "Veet, veet, veet" could be heard on the porch! A quick count of little heads proved that the entire family had come home. They were swooping and calling! They had so much to talk about!

Two tired little swallows climbed into the now too-small nest. The other three little swallows lined up next to the nest on the porch beam with their heads tucked underneath their wings. A good night's sleep for all and a job well done for the parents!

As the warm summer days passed, the little birds grew into beautiful barn swallows. Their dives and turns and cheerful calls and chatting continued. The swallow family always came together in the evening. And the people in the house always checked to make sure they were on the side porch before they went to bed. They loved the swallows dearly.

It's a very chilly morning.

"Veet, veet, veet—click, click, click," it's time to fly south for the winter. The barn swallows flew around the house calling loudly. Before long, other barn swallows from barns and houses nearby joined them in a large group. They all perched with their families in trees and power lines overhead.

All their voices were chirping and clicking together. A great flock of barn swallows flew up into the sky together to begin their long journey to warmer southern places.

The people watched the barn swallows that had become such a part of their family fly away. They were very lucky to have them live on the side porch for the summer months. Barn swallows have a great sense of home and family that earned the people's respect and admiration.

Goodbye little friends. We'll see you next year! Have a safe trip! X.O.

"There is another, a greater stream which this little one will teach you much about,
the stream of life, home is the starting place and love the guide to your actions."

—J. Alden Weir to Alden Twachtman (the son of American Impressionist John Twachtman), January 3, 1892